Get the Most Out of It

BRITANNICA

Mathematics in Context

Britannica

Mathematics in Context is a comprehensive curriculum for the middle grades. It was developed in collaboration with the Wisconsin Center for Education Research, School of Education, University of Wisconsin–Madison and the Freudenthal Institute at the University of Utrecht, The Netherlands, with the support of National Science Foundation Grant No. 9054928.

 National Science Foundation

Opinions expressed are those of the authors
and not necessarily those of the Foundation

Revision Project

Peter Sickler
Project Director

Teri Hedges
Revision Consultant

Nieka Mamczak
Revision Consultant

Erin Turner
Revision Consultant

Cheryl Deese
MiC General Manager

Vicki Mirabile
Project Manager

ISBN 0-03-071623-3

1 2 3 4 5   303   05 04 03 02

The *Mathematics in Context* Development Team

Mathematics in Context is a comprehensive curriculum for the middle grades. The National Science Foundation funded the National Center for Research in Mathematical Sciences Education at the University of Wisconsin–Madison to develop and field-test the materials from 1991 through 1996. The Freudenthal Institute at the University of Utrecht in The Netherlands, as a subcontractor, collaborated with the University of Wisconsin–Madison on the development of the curriculum.

The initial version of *Get the Most Out of It* was developed by Anton Roodhardt, and Martin Kindt. It was adapted for use in American schools by Margaret A. Pligge and Aaron N. Simon.

National Center for Research in Mathematical Sciences Education Staff

Thomas A. Romberg
Director

Joan Daniels Pedro
Assistant to the Director

Gail Burrill
Coordinator
Field Test Materials

Margaret R. Meyer
Coordinator
Pilot Test Materials

Mary Ann Fix
Editorial Coordinator

Sherian Foster
Editorial Coordinator

James A. Middleton
Pilot Test Coordinator

Margaret A. Pligge
First Edition Coordinator

Project Staff

Jonathan Brendefur
Laura J. Brinker
James Browne
Jack Burrill
Rose Byrd
Peter Christiansen
Barbara Clarke
Doug Clarke
Beth R. Cole

Fae Dremock
Jasmina Milinkovic
Kay Schultz
Mary C. Shafer
Julia A. Shew
Aaron N. Simon
Marvin Smith
Stephanie Z. Smith
Mary S. Spence
Kathleen A. Steele

Freudenthal Institute Staff

Jan de Lange
Director

Els Feijs
Coordinator

Martin van Reeuwijk
Coordinator

Project Staff

Mieke Abels
Nina Boswinkel
Frans van Galen
Koeno Gravemeijer
Marja van den Heuvel-Panhuizen
Jan Auke de Jong
Vincent Jonker
Ronald Keijzer

Martin Kindt
Jansie Niehaus
Nanda Querelle
Anton Roodhardt
Leen Streefland
Adri Treffers
Monica Wijers
Astrid de Wild

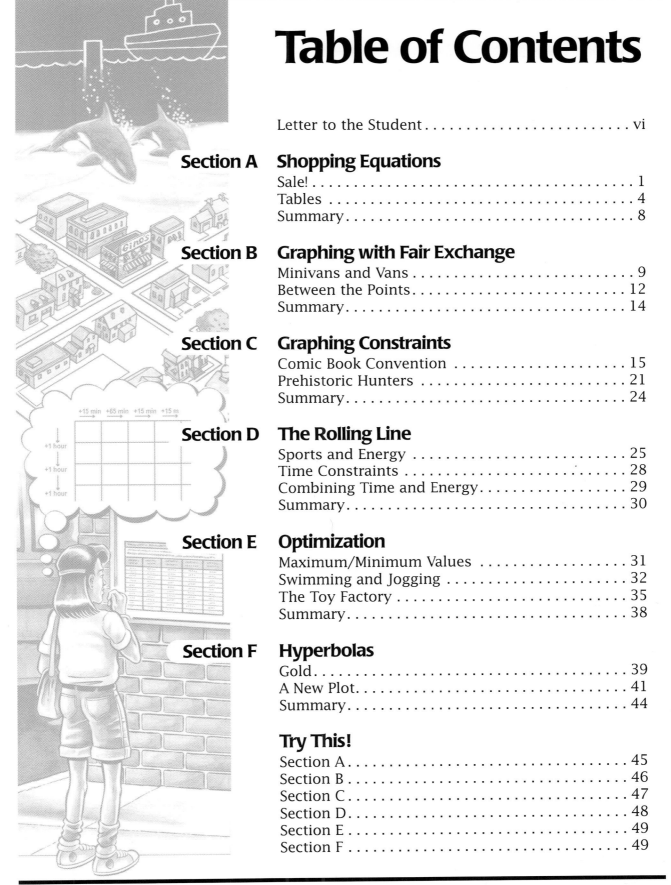

Table of Contents

Dear Student,

Welcome to the unit *Get the Most Out of It*. Have you ever planned a trip for a large number of people? One of the topics you will study in this unit is how to plan a camping field trip for the eighth grade. You will need to consider different ways to transport 96 people and all of their camping gear. You will find many solutions to this problem, and you will investigate to find the solution that has the smallest cost.

In this unit, you will use graphs to help you solve problems. You will investigate booth space at a comic book convention, and you will find the best exercise program that uses a limited amount of time. Also, you will explore how prehistoric hunters made optimal use of their hunting territories.

When you are finished, you will have learned some important ideas about how to solve problems using ideas from algebra.

We hope you enjoy the unit.

Sincerely,

The Mathematics in Context Development Team

Antonio and Jason are friends. Their favorite store, which sells only jeans and T-shirts, is having a gigantic sale. Antonio and Jason have saved some money, and they are ready to shop! For this sale, all T-shirts have one price and all jeans have one price.

Antonio buys two jeans and five T-shirts for $154.

1. a. Find a possible per-item price for jeans and for T-shirts.

   b. Are other prices possible? Explain your answer.

   c. Is it possible that the price of a T-shirt is $32? Explain why or why not.

2. a. What is the cost of four pairs of jeans and ten T-shirts?

   b. What are some other purchases for which you know the cost?

You can write a "shopping equation" for Antonio's purchase. If J stands for the jeans price and T for the T-shirt price, you can write:

$$2J + 5T = 154$$

This shopping equation is an example of an equation with two unknowns.

3. What shopping equation describes the price of four pairs of jeans and ten T-shirts? How is it related to the original shopping equation?

The equation $2J + 5T = 154$ is true for many values for J and T.

4. Check that the number pair $J = 52$ and $T = 10$ makes the equation true. Find three other number pairs that work.

5. Another number pair that works for the equation is $J = 82$ and $T = -2$.

    a. Explain why these values do not make sense for this problem.

    b. Describe the ranges of values for J and T that make sense for this equation.

Values for J and T that make the equation true are called *solutions* to the equation.

6. Jason buys three pairs of jeans and four T-shirts. The total cost is $182.

    a. Write a shopping equation for Jason's purchase.

    b. Find three solutions without considering Antonio's purchase.

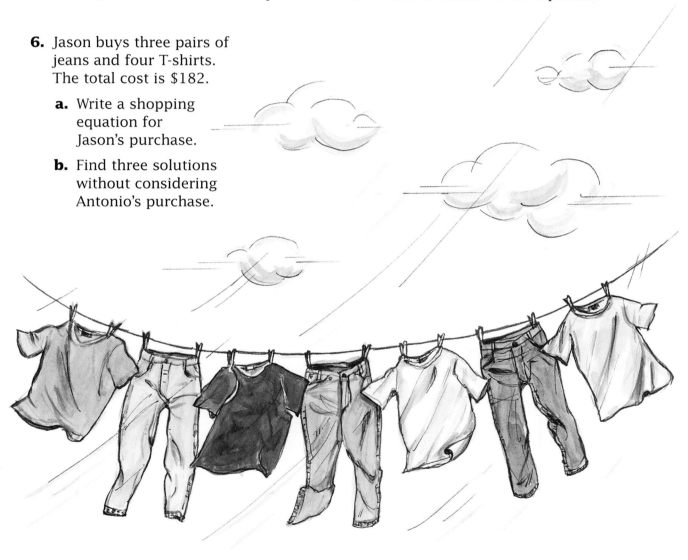

7. Look back at the information you have for Antonio's and Jason's purchases. Using that information, find the prices for one T-shirt and one pair of jeans.

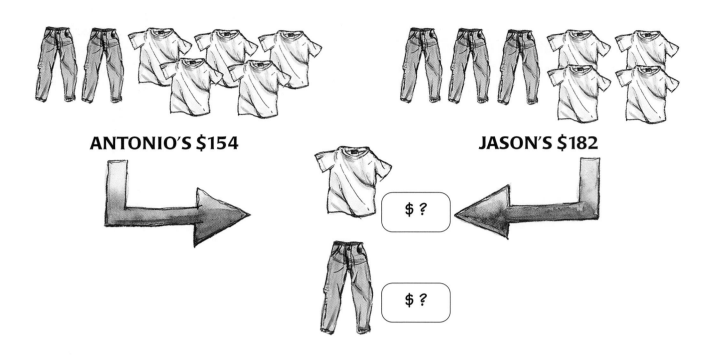

ANTONIO'S $154   **JASON'S $182**

$?

$?

TABLES

In the *Comparing Quantities* unit, you developed several strategies to solve similar shopping problems. For one strategy, called "notebook notation," information is organized in a table.

Hannah solved problem **7** using the notebook notation method, as shown on the right.

8. Explain Hannah's solution.

9. Copy Hannah's table and write an equation for each row in the table.

	J	T	Price
Antonio's purchase	2	5	154
Jason's purchase	3	4	182
	6	15	462
	6	8	364
	0	7	98
	0	1	14
	0	5	70
	2	0	84
	1	0	42

Selena discovered her own way to solve problem **7**.

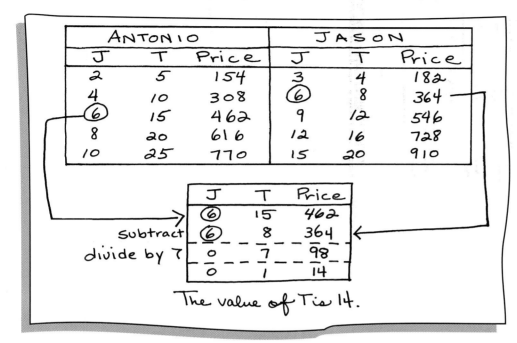

10. a. Explain Selena's strategy.

b. Describe how you can find the value of *J*.

11. Bard's Used Book Store is having a sale on paperback books and audio books (books on tape). All the books on sale are one price, and all the audio books on sale are one price. Amera buys two books and five audio books for $46. Beth buys six books and three audio books for $42. Find the price of one book and the price of one audio book.

12. The Dial Shop has one price for any watch and one price for any radio. Five watches and four radios cost $134. Four watches and five radios cost $127. Find the price of one watch and the price of one radio.

Below is another way to look at Selena's strategy from page 5. While it uses equations, it is still the same strategy.

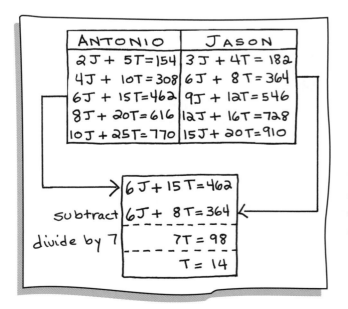

13. a. You can find the value of J by combining the equations $8J + 20T = 616$ and $15J + 20T = 910$. Show how.

b. Once you know that $T = 14$, there is another way to find the value of J. Show how.

In problem **13**, you found a pair of values that satisfies both equations. The pair of values is called a *common solution* for the two equations.

14. a. Find a common solution for the two equations $X + 2Y = 95$ and $X + Y = 55$. Is there more than *one* common solution?

    b. Do the equations $X + 2Y = 95$ and $3X + 6Y = 290$ have a common solution? Explain.

    c. Is there a common solution for these three equations: $X + 2Y = 95$, $X + Y = 55$, and $3X + Y = 110$? Explain your answer.

    d. Sandy thinks three equations can never have a common solution. Explain why you agree or disagree with Sandy.

15. A bill for two glasses of cranberry juice and three glasses of orange juice is $5.20. Another bill for four glasses of cranberry juice and six glasses of orange juice is $10.40.

    a. Explain why it is not possible to find the price of one glass of cranberry juice.

    b. Suppose the price of one glass of orange juice is 40 cents more than the price of one glass of cranberry juice. What is the price of one glass of cranberry juice?

Summary

In this section, you solved shopping problems. You used both a table (notebook notation) and equations to solve the problems.

The equation $2X + 5Y = 100$ has two unknowns, so it has many solutions. When a pair of values satisfies two equations with two unknowns, that pair of values is a *common solution.*

Summary Questions

Here are two equations with two unknowns:

$$2X + 5Y = 100$$

$$3X + 8Y = 156$$

16. This pair of equations has one common solution. Find it using a method discussed in this section.

17. Does every pair of equations with two unknowns have one common solution? Give examples to justify your answer.

MINIVANS and VANS

Eighth-grade students from Wingra Middle School are going on a camping trip. There will be 96 people going, including the students and teachers. All the luggage, gear, and supplies are already packed into 64 equal-sized boxes. Now the organizers want to rent the right number of vehicles to take everyone to the campsite. They can choose between two different types of vehicles from a car rental agency:

| **Minivan** | **Van** |

| **Seats 6 people**
 Cargo space: 5 boxes | **Seats 8 people**
 Cargo space: 4 boxes |

1. **a.** If the organizers decide to rent only vans, how many do they need? For safety reasons, no boxes can be placed on the seats.

   b. If the organizers rent only vans, how could they arrange to give people more room?

2. What is different if they rent only minivans? What is the same?

The organizers want to minimize the number of drivers. They think it may be possible to fit all the campers and boxes into fewer vehicles if they rent a combination of minivans and vans.

In the *Decision Making* unit, you worked with a method called *fair exchange* to find solutions to problems like this one. Using this method, the first step is to think about just the number of people and not the number of boxes.

For exactly 96 people, there are several possibilities for renting minivans and vans. One solution is 16 minivans, 0 vans.

3. a. When considering just the people, a fair exchange for this problem is to exchange 4 minivans for 3 vans. Why does this work?

b. List all the possible combinations of minivans and vans that carry exactly 96 people.

c. Check two of your combinations to make sure that each one carries 96 people.

Now consider only the number of boxes.

4. a. What is a fair exchange between minivans and vans for the boxes?

    b. List all the possible combinations of minivans and vans that hold exactly 64 boxes.

5. Compare the solutions for the people and the boxes. What combination of vehicles would you recommend to the camping organizers?

Between·the·Points

Using fair exchange may become difficult for larger numbers. Another approach is to use a graph.

One solution for carrying 96 people is the number pair: $(M, V) = (4, 9)$.

M stands for the number of minivans and *V* for the number of vans. In the diagram below, the point (4, 9) is marked with a small circle.

6. a. What does the combination (4, 9) mean?

   b. Draw a graph and use small circles to mark other combinations that satisfy the people requirement. (*Hint:* You can look back to problem **3.**)

   c. How could fair exchange be used to graph the points?

   d. All of these points are on a single line. Explain why most of the other points on this line won't work.

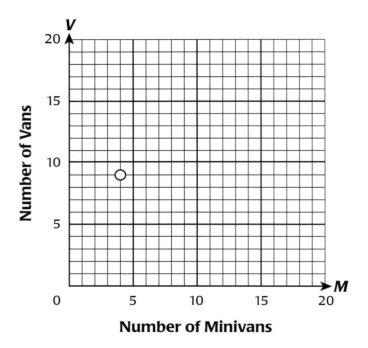

7. On the same graph, use "×'s" to mark the combinations that work for the boxes requirement. (*Hint:* You can look back to problem **4.**)

8. Describe what the graph tells you about transportation for the camping trip.

9. One of the students says, "We should rent 14 vehicles." Is this correct?

When you use graphing to solve a fair exchange problem, sometimes the coordinates of the solution may not be integers, or sometimes the lines may form a small angle, like this:

For these reasons, it can be difficult to read an exact solution from a graph. To find an exact solution, you can use equations.

For the transportation problem, an equation that describes the requirement for moving people is:

$$M \times 6 + V \times 8 = 96$$

10. Explain all the numbers and symbols in the above equation.

Raphael wrote $6M + 8V = 96$.

11. Is Raphael's people-equation the same as the one in problem **10?** Explain.

12. a. Now think about the requirement for moving the boxes. Write a boxes-equation for this problem.

    b. Explain all the numbers and symbols in your boxes-equation.

If you write your equations like Raphael, you get two equations that look like those used to solve the shopping problems. You can solve these equations as you did in Section A to find the common solution.

13. Find the common solution of the two equations. Check that your answer matches your graph solution.

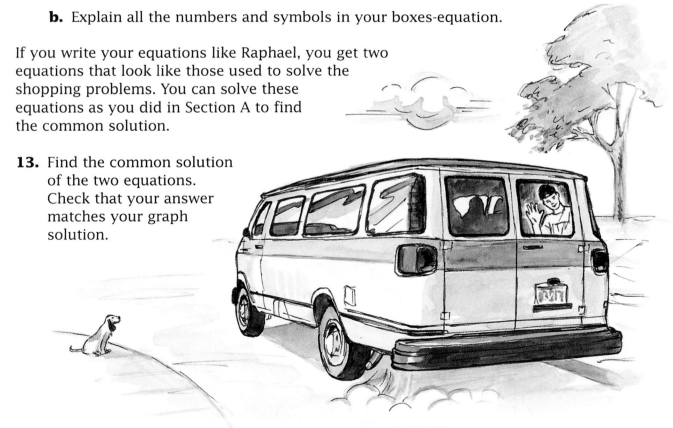

Summary

In this section, you found solutions to a rental problem. As one method, you found a few combinations of vans and minivans that worked for each of two different requirements (boxes and people). You graphed more solutions using the fair exchange principle. Then you used two lines to find a common solution. As another method, you wrote equations for boxes and for people and then solved for a common solution by treating them as shopping equations.

Summary Questions

14. What does *fair exchange* mean? Use an example as part of your explanation.

Consider the following equation: $2X + 5Y = 100$.

15. **a.** Find some (X, Y) combinations that are solutions of the equation.

   b. Draw the graph of the equation. Explain how you did this.

   c. Describe how you can illustrate fair exchange in your graph.

16. **a.** Draw the graph for the equation $5X + 2Y = 82$ on the same graph as problem **15.**

   b. What is the common solution for the two equations?

Comic Book Convention

Comic book dealers are organizing a comic book convention. There are two available locations.

1. If you were a member of the convention planning committee, what factors would you consider in choosing a building for the convention?

Large Booth   **Regular Booth**

Each dealer will have a booth. Some dealers have more comic books than others, and want larger booths. The convention planning committee will make booths available in two sizes to the dealers, regular (3-meter length) and large (5-meter length), as shown above.

One building under consideration is the Moore Civic Center. There, the total possible length for all booths is 600 meters.

2. a. What is the maximum number of regular booths that can be used?

   b. What is the maximum number of large booths that can be used?

   c. If the convention has the same number of regular and large booths, what is the maximum number of booths at the convention?

   d. Find two other possible combinations of regular booths and large booths that use all 600 meters.

An equation that describes the numbers of regular and large booths that use all 600 meters is:

$$R \times 3 + L \times 5 = 600, \text{ or } 3R + 5L = 600$$

3. a. Explain all the numbers and symbols in the equation above.

   b. Check that the solutions you found in problem **2d** satisfy this equation.

   c. Describe a fair exchange for booths and use it to find another solution.

   d. What is a fair exchange that uses larger numbers of the two types of booths?

The graph below shows the solution $(R, L) = (150, 30)$ for the Moore Civic Center.

4. a. Copy the graph on a sheet of graph paper. Using the fair exchange you found for problem **3d,** plot some more combinations of regular and large booths.

   b. Are there solutions other than the ones you plotted? Explain how you know.

   c. Draw the line connecting your solutions. Is every point on this line a solution? Explain your answer.

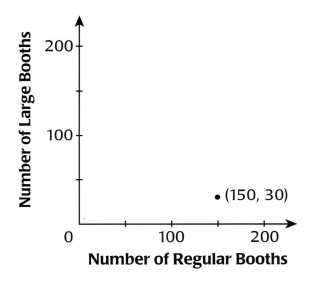

It is a month before the convention, and 150 dealers have reserved booths.

5. a. On your graph, show all possible combinations of regular and large booths that total 150 booths.

   b. Write an equation for all possible combinations for 150 booths.

   c. Is it possible to have a combination for 150 booths that uses exactly 600 meters? If so, how many regular booths are in this combination?

Looking at the floor plan for the Moore Civic Center, one of the planning committee members realizes that she doesn't need to use all 600 meters. The total length needed for the booths can be *less than or equal to* 600 meters. She writes:

$$3R + 5L \leq 600$$

This is called an *inequality*.

The symbol $\leq$ is a combination of the symbols $<$ and $=$. It means "is less than or equal to." You can also read the inequality as "$3R + 5L$ is at most 600."

The inequality is sometimes called a *constraint* because it *constrains* (limits) the possible solutions. Below is a graph for the inequality, or constraint, from above. The graph of $3R + 5L = 600$ is a line. The graph of $3R + 5L \leq 600$ includes both the shaded region and the line.

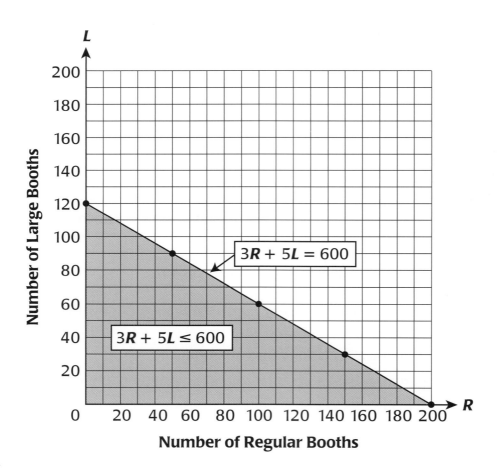

6. a. Describe the region for the inequality $3R + 5L \geq 600$.

b. Write an inequality for this constraint: The total number of booths is at most 150.

c. Graph the region for the inequality in part **b.** (Use the same graph you made for problem **5.**)

Of the 150 dealers who have reserved booths, 120 want regular booths. The others want large booths.

7. a. Is it possible to hold the convention at the Moore Civic Center under these constraints? Explain your answer.

　　b. Answer part **a** if the reservations were the other way around, and 120 dealers wanted large booths.

　　c. Describe how you can use your graph from problems **4, 5,** and **6** to verify your answers to parts **a** and **b.**

One week later, a total of 180 dealers have requested a booth at the convention.

8. a. Write an equation using R and L to describe this situation.

　　b. Graph all possible solutions to your equation on the graph you've been working with.

　　c. Compare this line with the line you drew for problem **5a.**

9. a. Is the Moore Civic Center still large enough for the convention? Be very specific: consider which combinations of regular and large booths are possible and which are not.

　　b. What is the maximum total number of booths that can fit in the Moore Civic Center? How can you use your graph to verify your answer?

With two planning days left, the number of booth reservations is at least 250. The organizers found a larger hall, the Kirby Convention Center, that allows 900 meters for all the booths.

The constraints for the convention can be formulated as follows:

Constraint I: The Kirby Convention Center allows at most 900 meters for all the booths.

Constraint II: The total number of booths is at least 250.

Constraint III: The number of regular booths is less than 200.

10. Write each constraint as an inequality.

The comic book vendors and the organizers are considering the following questions:

What are the maximum and minimum numbers of booths possible?

Is it possible to have equal numbers of large booths and regular booths?

Is it possible to have twice as many large booths as regular booths?

Is it possible to have twice as many regular booths as large booths?

You can find the answers to these questions by looking at the *feasible region* on a graph. The feasible region is the part of a graph that satisfies all the constraints.

11. a. On a single graph, show the borderline for each constraint.

b. The feasible region has a triangular shape. Find the coordinates of the vertices of this triangle.

c. Write a paragraph to answer the four questions above. Refer to your graph to justify your answers.

PREHISTORIC HUNTERS

In prehistoric times, people lived in small communities. Archaeologists who study how prehistoric people lived want to know the sizes of their communities. Since the communities existed so long ago, the archaeologists have to work from clues and theories. In the rest of this section, you will see how scientists use feasible regions to solve these problems.

Archaeologists start with a simple theory: the area (A) of a hunting ground can tell us something about the number of people (N) in the community.

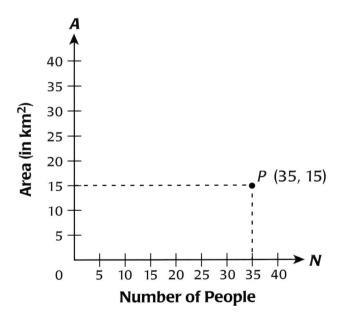

On the graph at the left, the coordinates (35, 15) of point *P* represent a community of 35 people who have a hunting area of 15 square kilometers. Points on the graph will be referred to as "situations." In some situations a group could survive, while in other situations a group could not survive.

Suppose (35, 15) represents a bad situation for a community because the hunting area is not large enough to supply the number of people with food.

12. a. List two situations that are worse. Explain why you think they are worse.

  b. What changes could occur to improve the situation?

Archaeologists know that a hunting area must be large enough to supply the people with food. It is possible to make a rough estimate of the area needed for a given number of people.

13. What would you need to know in order to estimate this?

The shaded region on the graph at the right (including the borderline) contains all the situations with sufficient food. In this respect, they are good situations.

14. a. Explain why the shading is above the borderline rather than below it.

    b. Why do you think the border is a straight line?

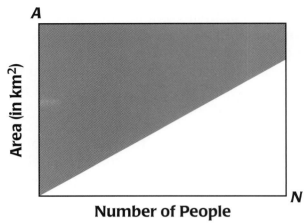

Expanding a hunting area could be difficult. A large hunting ground would provide more food, but it also had to be defended against hunters from other settlements. Archaeologists estimate the area that could be defended by N people.

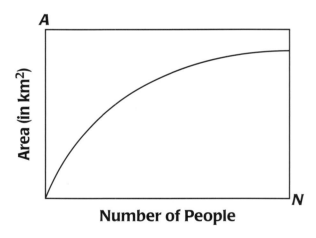

The graph above shows the maximum area that could be defended by different numbers of people. Notice that the borderline is curved.

15. a. Explain why the borderline is curved.

    b. Copy the graph. If you consider only defending the land, without worrying about food, which part of the graph represents the good situations? Shade that part.

Combining the two graphs into one diagram creates four regions, as shown at the right.

16. **a.** For each region (**I–IV**), explain whether it represents a good or bad situation for the community.

  b. Approximate the number of people in the largest community that could survive.

  c. Approximate the number of people in the largest community that could survive if its hunting area was 14 square kilometers.

  d. What if 20 square kilometers of hunting area was available?

  e. What about 25 square kilometers?

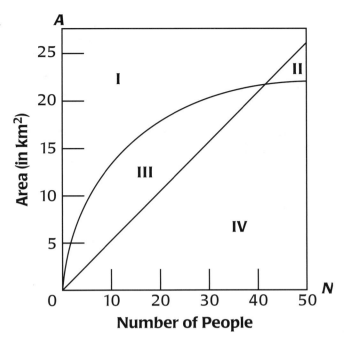

Archaeologists use the size of the largest group that could survive as an estimate of the size of the community.

17. **a.** What factors might affect the accuracy of the archaeologists' estimate.

Archaeologists claim that a community larger or smaller than this estimate would gradually return to the estimated number.

  b. Try to find at least a partial explanation for their claim. (*Hint:* Start by selecting a point in each region and discuss the future of the community it represents.)

Summary

In this section, you used constraints to draw graphs and find feasible regions for a problem. You used equations and inequalities to represent the constraints.

To solve a problem, you first write equations and inequalities.

To graph a feasible region:

- draw the borderline(s)

- decide which side of the borderline contains "favorable" points

- shade the feasible region

Some feasible regions have borders that are curves rather than straight lines.

Summary Questions

Here is an example of a constraint:

$$X + 2Y \leq 10$$

18. a. Create a problem for which the inequality above is a constraint.

b. Is it possible for your X and Y to be negative? Describe the range of possible values for your X and Y.

c. Give four possible solutions to your problem.

d. Give a solution of $X + 2Y \leq 10$ that is not a solution of $X + 2Y < 10$.

19. Graph the feasible region for the following constraints. X and Y are not negative.

$$X + 2Y \leq 10$$

$$2X + Y \leq 10$$

$$X + Y \geq 3$$

Sports and Energy

To stay healthy, the energy you expend in everyday activities and the energy you get from the food you eat should be in balance. Energy can be measured in calories.

Walking: 5 calories/minute   **Cycling: 11 calories/minute**

1. Look up the word *calorie* in the dictionary. Rewrite the dictionary definition in your own words.

When you eat, your body takes in calories. For example, one apple provides about 70 calories, and one banana provides about 140 calories. Walking, cycling, and other forms of exercise use energy. Information about calories can help you make decisions about food and exercise.

Use the data above for problems **2** and **3**.

2. **a.** How long do you have to walk to use 1,000 calories?

   b. How long do you have to cycle to use 1,000 calories?

3. Mark's weekly exercise program combines 90 minutes of walking with 50 minutes of cycling. How many calories does Mark use per week on this program?

There are many ways to combine walking and cycling in a program that uses 1,000 calories.

4. **a.** Write an equation describing programs of walking and cycling that use 1,000 calories. Use *W* for the number of walking minutes and *C* for the number of cycling minutes. Explain all the numbers and symbols in your equation.

b. Graph your equation on graph paper. Use the horizontal axis for *W* and the vertical axis for *C*. Label the graphed line with the total number of calories.

c. Why do all the points on the graph you drew for part **b** work? Explain.

d. What is an equation for combinations of walking and cycling that use 800 calories? Draw and label the line on the same graph you drew for part **b.**

e. What are equations for programs that use 600, 400, and 200 calories? Draw and label the line for each equation on the same graph.

Walking: 5 calories/minute

Cycling: 11 calories/minute

Your graph for problem **4** should be a set of parallel lines, as shown below. Each line represents all the combinations for one level of energy.

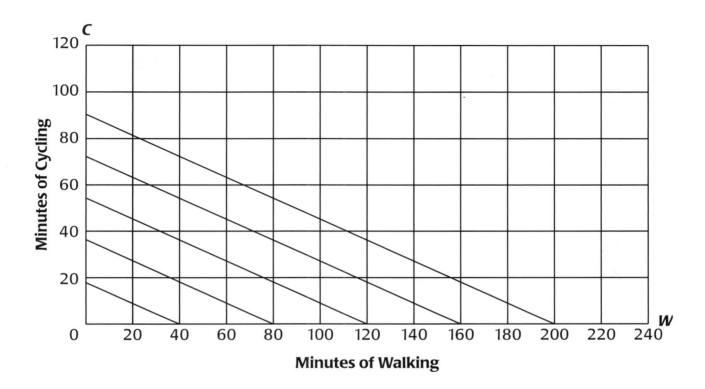

Place a pencil (or toothpick) on one of the lines.

5. What can you say about all the programs that lie along this line?

Roll the pencil until it rests along another energy line.

6. In which direction do you move your pencil to get to a higher amount of energy? Explain.

7. Which exercise program, (40, 40) or (56, 28), uses more energy? Describe two different ways to find an answer.

TIME CONSTRAINTS

Warner Stewart likes to exercise by walking and cycling outdoors. He always exercises during his lunch break.

8. a. Suppose he has at most 30 minutes during lunch to exercise. Draw and shade a graph to show all possible programs he can use. Label the graph with an equation or inequality.

   b. Select three programs of exercise by drawing three points in the shaded region of the graph you drew for part **a.**

   c. Draw a line on your graph that represents programs that use 200 calories. Put a pencil (or toothpick) on the line. Roll the pencil to decide whether the programs you selected in part **b** use different energies.

Markie Engle is training for a competition. She walks and cycles between 100 and 150 minutes a day. These constraints can be written as two inequalities:

$$W + C \geq 100 \text{ and } W + C \leq 150$$

9. Graph all the programs that fulfill the two constraints.

Markie decides that she never wants to spend less than an hour either walking or cycling.

10. a. Draw her complete feasible region.

   b. What are the coordinates of the vertices of the feasible region?

   c. What is a good program for Markie? How much energy does it use?

   d. Are all the constraints necessary for finding the feasible region?

Combining TIME and ENERGY

You can use a rolling energy line to find the energy spent in different programs. You will look only at programs in the feasible region. Look at the feasible region from the graph you made for problem **10.**

11. a. The point $P(70, 70)$ is in the feasible region for Markie Engle. For this program, find the time spent walking, the time spent cycling, the total time, and the energy used.

   b. All the programs that use 1,120 calories lie along a line. Add this energy line to your graph from problem **10a.** What equation corresponds to this line?

Use the energy line from problem **11b** as the starting position for a rolling line. The energy line can be rolled onto other points in the feasible region.

12. a. Roll the energy line to a position closer to the origin. Describe the energy for programs on your new line.

   b. Which program satisfies all constraints and uses the minimum amount of energy? How much energy does it use?

   c. Which program uses the maximum amount of energy? How much energy does it use?

For Markie Engle's exercise program, you worked with four constraints:

   I. $W \geq 60$ **III.** $W + C \geq 100$

   II. $C \geq 60$ **IV.** $W + C \leq 150$

13. a. A small change in the constraints may result in a different feasible region. What would happen if you changed constraint **I** by a small amount? Use your graph to investigate.

   b. Make small changes in the other three constraints. Explain your results.

Summary

In this section, you looked at constraints that form feasible regions. To find a program that uses the maximum or minimum amount of energy within a feasible region, you used a rolling energy line. You looked at energy values for points on the line and in the feasible region.

Summary Questions

The graph at the right shows two features of a program of walking and cycling. In the graph, energy is measured in calories and time is measured in minutes.

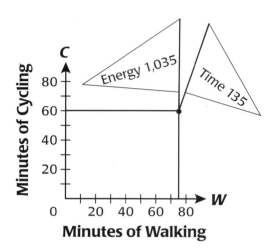

14. Write everything you know about this exercise program.

15. Look at all programs that use a total of 135 minutes. How can these programs be represented in the graph? How can they be represented with an equation?

16. How can all programs with 1,035 calories be represented in the graph? How can they be represented with an equation?

17. What do other energy values have to do with a rolling line?

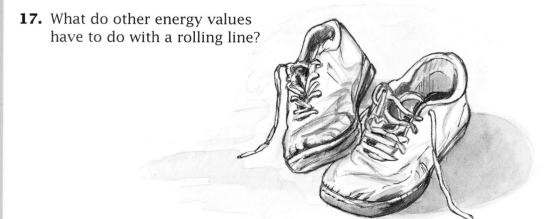

Maximum / Minimum Values

Finding a maximum or a minimum value under particular constraints is called an *optimization problem.* The optimization problems in this section are similar to those you worked on in the last section.

In the last section, time and energy constraints led to a triangular feasible region. Points inside or on the triangle satisfied all the constraints; points outside the triangle did not satisfy the constraints.

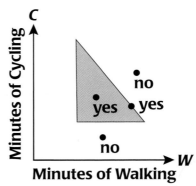

For each point, you can find values for *W*, *C*, and the amount of energy spent. The diagram below shows how different values for walking minutes and cycling minutes would give different energy values.

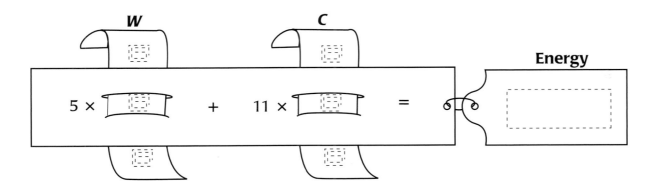

This diagram is just like the equation for energy that you saw in the previous section. When any (*W, C*) pair from the feasible region is "plugged in" to the formula, the result is the energy value for that program.

To find the program with the highest or lowest energy value, you might think you would have to try *every* program in the feasible region. Think how long that would take! However, in the previous section you saw how to use a rolling line to quickly find the programs for the maximum and the minimum energy values.

1. Look back at Markie Engle's exercise programs. Explain how a rolling line was used to find her maximum and minimum energy programs.

Swimming and Jogging

Margie is in training. She wants to maximize the energy she uses in a program of swimming and jogging.

She wants to exercise for at least 90 minutes and at most 150 minutes. Also, she wants to jog for at least twice as long as she swims.

2. a. Write Margie's situation as three constraints. Use S to represent the number of minutes swimming and J to represent the number of minutes jogging.

   b. Graph the feasible region, making the horizontal axis the S-axis.

   c. Find the coordinates for the vertices of the feasible region.

   d. What is the longest time Margie can spend swimming and still follow her plan? What is the longest time she can spend jogging?

Margie uses 13 calories per minute swimming and 9 calories per minute jogging.

3. a. Draw the line showing all programs that use 1,300 calories on the same graph you created in problem **2.** Use a "flag" to label the line.

   b. Use a rolling line to find the program for Margie that uses the maximum amount of energy.

   c. What is the amount of energy used for that program?

The line showing all programs that use a certain number of calories is represented by the equation $13S + 9J = E$. The letter E stands for the energy value for all programs on the line.

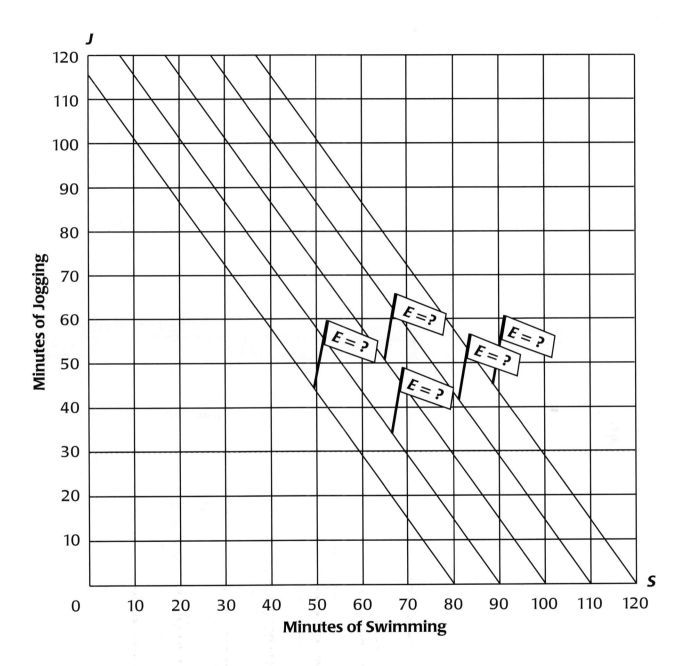

4. Find the energy value for each line in the graph above.

For every position of the rolling line, $13S + 9J$ has a different value. This means the equation for the rolling line is $13S + 9J = E$. *Note*: $13S + 9J = 1,300$ represents one energy line, while $13S + 9J = E$ represents a family of energy lines.

Each diagram below represents a feasible region for a list of constraints. The axes are labeled with the general symbols *x* and *y*.

Each graph shows the starting position for a rolling line. At the top of each graph is the flag-equation for the rolling line (labeled with an *F*).

a.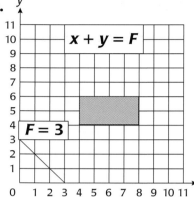

b.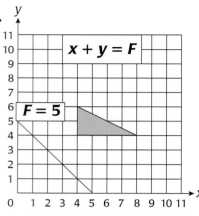

c.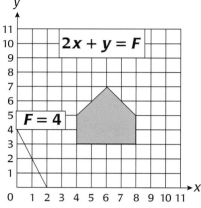

d.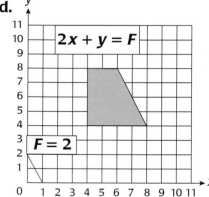

e.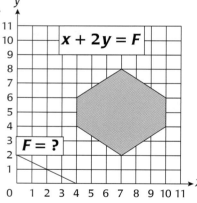

f.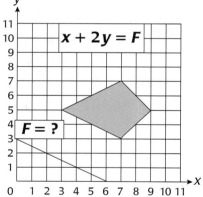

Use Student Activity Sheet 1 to answer questions 5 and 6.

5. a. For each graph, draw the positions of the rolling line that contain the maximum and minimum *F* values in the feasible regions.

   b. Compute the minimum and maximum *F* values for each feasible region.

6. What do you notice about where the maximum and minimum values occur in each feasible region?

The TOY FACTORY

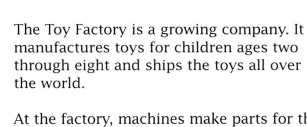

The Toy Factory is a growing company. It manufactures toys for children ages two through eight and ships the toys all over the world.

At the factory, machines make parts for the toys. Some of the parts are delivered by truck to home workers for assembly. Other parts are assembled by workers at the factory. Some of the factory assembly tasks are more complex, so a factory worker earns a higher wage than a home worker.

7. Why do you think a company would use both home workers and factory workers?

Here is one of the main problems for the managers of the factory:

How should we divide the labor between the two groups?

Here is some more information to help the managers solve this problem:

- All workers complete several short shifts of work each day.
- In a shift, a home worker can fill 10 boxes, and a factory worker can fill 12 boxes. The managers want to produce at least 6,000 boxes per shift.
- There are 250 factory workers now. The company can hire up to a maximum of 450 workers in the factory.

There are two other issues related to home workers:

- The company guarantees work for 200 home workers and hires more as needed.
- The company has enough trucks to carry parts and boxes for no more than 400 home workers.

8. If you read the problem carefully, you can find four constraints for this problem.

    a. Write the four constraints in a mathematical way. Use the symbols F and H for the numbers of factory workers and home workers.

    b. Copy the graph below and graph the feasible region.

The managers can choose any point in the feasible region, and then calculate a cost for each pair of coordinates (*F, H*). They know that each factory worker costs the factory $50 per shift and that each home worker costs the factory $30 per shift. Using *C* for the total cost, the rolling line equation is $50F + 30H = C$.

9. a. Graph the equation $C = 15,000$.

   b. If you were a manager, what would you try to minimize? What would you want to maximize?

10. How many factory workers and how many home workers would you recommend for the factory? Why?

11. For which of the four constraints do small changes *not* influence the minimum cost?

12. What could the managers do to raise production to 8,000 boxes per shift?

Summary

In this section, you solved optimization problems. In an optimization problem, you select from values for two or more unknowns to maximize or minimize some other value.

Summary Questions

13. List the steps needed to solve an optimization problem. Write these steps so that someone could follow your directions.

Below is a graph of a feasible region for a situation.

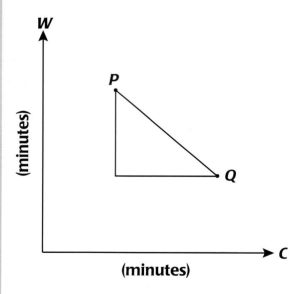

14. Could *P* give the maximum value for a rolling line equation? What about *Q*? Give reasons for your answers.

In Section C, you worked with a feasible region that has a curved border.

That is not uncommon in real-world problems. In this section, you will look at another problem involving a curve.

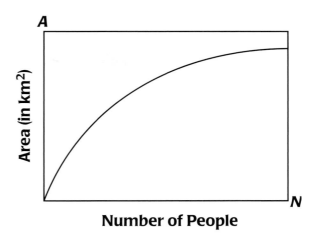

Number of People

Gold

In the 19th century, many adventurers traveled to North America to search for gold. A man named Dan Jackson owned some land where gold had been found. Instead of digging for the gold himself, he rented plots of land to the adventurers. The "rent" was to give Dan 50% of any gold found on the plot of land.

Dan gave each adventurer four stakes and a rope that was exactly 100 meters long. Each adventurer had to use the stakes and rope to mark off a rectangle with north-south and east-west sides.

1. Did everyone get the same area to dig for gold? Explain your answer.

There are many different rectangles you can make that have a perimeter of 100 meters.

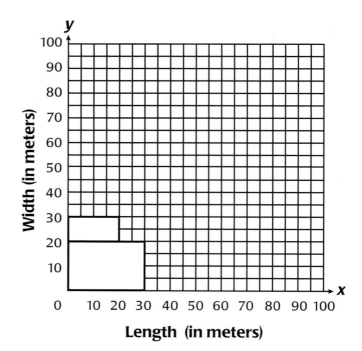

Width (in meters)

Length (in meters)

2. **a.** On graph paper, draw at least five different rectangles with perimeters of 100 meters. Draw your rectangles to scale, using one grid unit to represent five meters.

   b. Cut out the rectangles. Tape them on a graph so the lower-left corners lie on the origin. Use the same grid size as in part **a,** as shown at the right.

For each rectangle, only the upper-right vertex will not touch an axis.

3. You should notice that all the upper-right vertices of your rectangles seem to lie on a line. What is the equation of that line? Use *x* and *y* as the dimensions of the rectangles.

4. Calculate the area of each rectangle, and organize all of your information in a table.

One of the diggers discovered that one kind of rectangle always had the greatest area. He decided to sell the secret to other diggers.

5. What was the secret?

A New Plot

Once the secret was out, Dan changed his rental agreement. He still gave the adventurers four stakes, and they still marked off rectangles with north-south and east-west sides, but with a new constraint:

The rectangle had to have an *area* of 400 square meters.

Since the adventurers had to use their own rope to mark off the plot, they had to decide how long their rope should be.

6. a. Using graph paper, draw at least five different rectangles with areas of 400 square meters. Again, use the scale that one grid unit represents five meters. How long is the rope needed for each rectangle?

   b. As you did before, cut out the rectangles and tape them on grid paper so two sides lie on the axes.

You should notice that the upper-right vertices no longer lie on a straight line, but instead on a curve called a *hyperbola*.

7. Connect the points of the hyperbola on your grid paper. What equation using x and y corresponds to the hyperbola?

8. One adventurer made a rectangle with a perimeter of 208 meters (and an area of 400 square meters, of course). Find the dimensions of the rectangle.

9. Using as little rope as possible, how would you mark off a rectangle with an area of 400 square meters?

Here is another area situation.

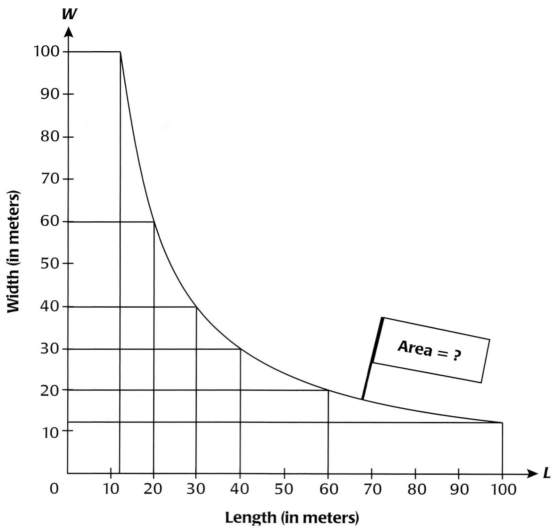

Length (in meters)

10. a. What is the area of each rectangle that fits directly beneath this hyperbola?

b. Write an equation for the hyperbola.

11. a. Draw a curve on graph paper that corresponds to rectangles that have areas of 600 square meters.

b. A rectangle has an area of 600 square meters and a perimeter of 140 meters. Use your graph to find its dimensions.

12. a. A rectangle has length L and width W. Two equations for the rectangle are $LW = 1,200$ and $L + W = 73$. What can you say about the area and perimeter of the rectangle?

b. Graph the two equations above. Use L for the horizontal axis.

c. Do any rectangle(s) satisfy both equations? If so, describe them; if not, explain why not.

d. Check your results from part **c** with calculations.

Here are two constraints for all rectangles with two sides along the axes:

I. The area is at least 900 square meters, and it is at most 1,200 square meters.

II. The horizontal side is at least 20 meters and it is at most 60 meters.

13. a. Graph the feasible region for these constraints.

b. Graph the line for the upper-right vertices for all rectangles with perimeters of 180 meters.

c. Use the rolling line strategy to find the rectangle that satisfies constraints **I** and **II** and minimizes the perimeter.

d. Do the same thing to find the rectangle with the maximum perimeter.

Summary

In this section, you investigated a curve called a hyperbola. You put all the rectangles with a fixed perimeter on the coordinate axes, and saw that their upper-right vertices lie on a line. Using all the rectangles with a fixed area, you saw that the upper-right vertices lie on a hyperbola.

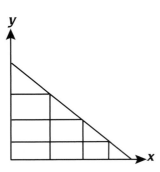

Rectangles with fixed perimeter: The upper-right vertices are on a straight line.

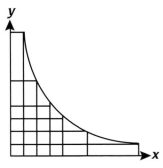

Rectangles with fixed area: The upper-right vertices are on a hyperbola.

Summary Questions

14. In the diagram above at the left, the perimeter of each rectangle is equal to 8 centimeters. What is the equation of the line?

15. In the diagram above at the right, the area of each rectangle is equal to 6 square centimeters. What is the equation of the hyperbola?

Two gold miners, Billy and Jesse, decide to cooperate. They have two 100-meter ropes. They think they can get more land if they tie their two ropes together than if they work separately.

16. What is your advice?

Section A. Shopping Equations

Here is an equation with two unknowns:

$$3P + 2R = 60$$

1. Make up a story that will fit this equation. Explain what each letter and number represents.

2. Check whether or not each of the following combinations is a solution for the equation $3P + 2R = 60$.

   a. $P = 10$ and $R = 15$

   b. $P = 15$ and $R = 22.5$

   c. $P = 20$ and $R = 1$

3. Find a different solution for the equation. Show that your solution fits.

4. Suppose $P = 5$. Find the value of R.

5. Here is another equation with the same variables: $7P + 3R = 110$. Find a common solution for this equation and the previous one.

Section B. Graphing with Fair Exchange

Josseline planned to make a terrace in her garden. She made a design with white and red tiles. For the whole terrace, she needs 100 white tiles and 65 red tiles. In the Rock Shop, she finds the type of tile she would like to use. The tiles are available in small and large packages. A small package contains five white and four red tiles, and a large package contains ten white and five red tiles.

1. **a.** If Josseline decides to buy only small packages, how many packages will she need?

   b. If Josseline buys only large packages, how many packages will she need?

   c. What is the disadvantage of each of the purchases mentioned in parts **a** and **b**?

Josseline decides to figure out whether a combination of packages will be better. If you consider only the number of white tiles, there are different possibilities to get exactly 100 white tiles.

2. Find two combinations of small packages *(S)* and large packages *(L)* that will give exactly 100 white tiles.

3. Explain why the equation for the white tiles can be written as $5S + 10L = 100$.

4. **a.** Draw a graph *(S, L)* of the white tiles.

   b. How can you use the fair exchange principal to draw the graph?

5. Now think about the red tiles only. Use *S* and *L* to write an equation that fits the number of red tiles.

6. Draw a graph of the red tiles equation on the same diagram as problem **4.**

7. How many small and how many large packages will be the best solution for Josseline's problem? Explain.

Section C. Graphing Constraints

A travel company wants to organize two different guided tours in a nature preserve. The travel agents want to organize short trips *(S)* of 2 hours and long trips *(L)* of 4 hours. There are already about 80 people who have made a reservation for one of the tours. There are five rangers available per day to guide the participants.

1. One constraint is that no ranger can work more than 8 hours per day. Explain why this constraint can be written as the following inequality:

    $$2S + 4L \leq 40$$

2. A second constraint is that every ranger has to work at least 4 hours per day. Write this constraint as an inequality.

3. Of the 80 people who have made a reservation, 25 want to take the long tour. The others did not state a preference. The size of any group that will make a long trip will be at most five. What is the third constraint?

4. Copy the graph below on a sheet of paper. Graph the borderlines of the three constraints and color the feasible region. Use the horizontal axis for *L* and the vertical axis for *S.*

5. The travel company would like to know the answers to the following questions. Use the graph you drew in problem **4** to justify your answers.

    a. What is the maximum number of trips possible?

    b. Is it possible to have an equal number of short trips and long trips?

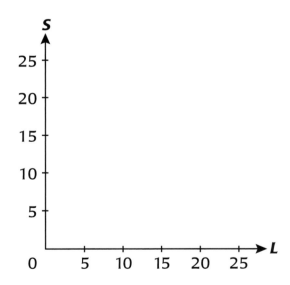

Section D. The Rolling Line

Joshua's doctor advised him to take extra calcium and iron. He prescribed a minimum of 50 milligrams of calcium and 8 milligrams of iron per day. In the store, two brands of tablets were available. Each tablet of brand *A* contains 5 milligrams of calcium and 2 milligrams of iron. Each tablet of brand *B* contains 10 milligrams of calcium and 1 milligram of iron.

1. How many tablets does Joshua have to take per day if he uses only brand *A*? How many if he uses only brand *B?*

Joshua decides to buy tablets of both brands, but how many of each does he have to take daily? In order to investigate this, he first looks at the minimum amount of calcium.

2. Explain why the inequality $5A + 10B \geq 50$ describes this constraint.

3. Write the inequality that represents the constraint that Joshua has to take a minimum of 8 milligrams of iron per day.

4. Use these inequalities to draw the feasible region on the graph paper.

Now that Joshua can see what combinations will give him the right amounts of calcium and iron, he is interested in the total number of tablets.

5. Draw a line through all combinations that have a total number of 12 tablets.

6. Take the line you drew in problem **5** as a starting position for the rolling line. Explain how you can use the rolling line to find the minimum number of tablets that Joshua can take.

7. Suppose Joshua's doctor prescribed a minimum of 10 milligrams of iron per day. Use your graph to investigate what would happen.

Section E. Optimization

Ian and his mother are going to fill bottles of mixed fruit juices to sell at a fair. Ian made up new names to put on the bottles: a bottle of Appsi is a mixture of 3 liters of apple juice and 1 liter of orange juice. A bottle of Nectar contains 2 liters of apple juice, 2 liters of orange juice, and 1 liter of peach juice. Ian and his mother have a supply of 240 liters of apple juice, 120 liters of orange juice, and 40 liters of peach juice. How can they find out what number of empty Appsi bottles and Nectar bottles to buy so they will use their whole supply of juices, or at least as much as possible?

You can find three constraints for this problem. The first constraint is determined by the amount of apple juice that is available and the amounts of apple juice that are used for a bottle of Appsi and for a bottle of Nectar.

1. Use the symbol A for the number of bottles of Appsi and the symbol N for the number of bottles of Nectar, and write this constraint in a mathematical way.

2. Write two other constraints using the symbols A and N.

3. Graph the feasible region on a sheet of graph paper.

Ian and his mother can sell each bottle with a profit of two dollars. Using P for the total profit, the rolling line equation is $2A + 2N = P$.

4. Graph the equation for $P = 80$ on the same graph you made in problem **3.**

5. What can you find out with the rolling line? What would you recommend to Ian and his mother?

Section F. Hyperbolas

1. Graph the feasible region for the following constraints for rectangles with two sides along the axes on a sheet of graph paper.

  I. The area is at least 400 square meters and at most 900 square meters.

  II. The perimeter is at least 100 meters and at most 140 meters.

CREDITS

Cover

Design by Ralph Paquet/Encyclopædia Britannica, Inc.

Collage by Koorosh Jamalpur/KJ Graphics.

Title Page

Design by Mickey Mankus/Navta Associates, Inc.; Illustration by L.S. Pierce/Navta Associates, Inc.

Illustrations

vi, 1-5, 7-11, 13, 15, 16, 19, 21, 23, 25, 26, 30, 35, 37, 39, 41, 43, 44 L.S. Pierce/Navta Associates, Inc.

Photographs

6 © Alan Becker/The Image Bank; **28** © Gregg Adams/Tony Stone Images; **29** © Frank Whitney/The Image Bank; **32** © Amwell/Tony Stone Images; **36** © Gary Gay/The Image Bank.

Development

Navta Associates, Inc.